Mr Peek's Poetry Fun time

Volume 2

To Evie

from

mr Peek

Something
NICE & NEW
From
Mr Peek's Poetry Place

BORROWED BOOKS

First published in 2018 by Borrowed Books, Hastings, UK.
Printed in China by Gold Printing,

A CIP record for this book is available from the British Library

ISBN

978-953-6374-98-4

Contents

Nice & New

Book

I opened up a picture book
And disappeared inside,
A world filled up with fun and games
Where I could stay and hide.

I laughed at silly creatures,
I giggled at funny words,
I let myself be carried away
By the songs of singing birds.

I read the book till way past late
Then I turned out my light,
To sleep and dream of all I'd seen
In my picture book that night.

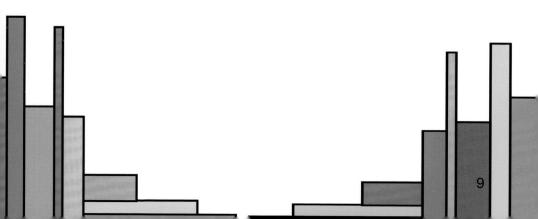

Marmalade

I don't want cheese, I don't want soup
I don't want fish from Guadaloupe,
I've said it now, my point is made
I just want toast with marmalade.

I don't want eggs, I don't want ham
I don't want baked beans served with jam,
You know the thing I'd love the most
Is marmalade on nice warm toast.

I don't want jars of pickled eggs
I don't want roasted leopards' legs,
All I want, again I say,
Is marmalade to start the day.

I love the way it spreads so thick
I love to eat it slow or quick,
I love its yummy, tangy taste
I hate to see it go to waste.

I love it oh so very much
I love its sticky, gooey touch,
I've loved it since I was quite small
When I get marmalade...
I eat it all.

Thoughtful Thinkers

Thirty-three thoughtful thinkers
Thought a thousand thoughtful things,
Thought of thunder, thought of thank you
Thought of thirty-thousand rings...

Thirty-three thousand thinkers
Thought of thirty thinking things,
Thought of thanking thirty thinkers
Thinking thoughts of thirty kings.

Be Good

Be good, be good, be good
Try to act the way you should,
Even though it's hard sometimes
Be good, be good, be good.

I had a friend, we'll call him Tom,
He was always good to me,
Now every time I think of him
I wish him well. Do you see?

The things we do they stay with us
Like our shadows on the ground,
They might hide in the darkness
But in the light of day they're found.

So if you want a happy life
Be good, be good, be good,
And even though it's hard sometimes
Try to act the way you should.

Puppy Dogs

I love all little puppy dogs
They are so cute and fun,
I love to watch them waddling
I love to watch them run.
I love the way they bounce around
I love to hear them bark,
I love to see them see themselves
In the windows after dark.

I love all little puppy dogs
I love the way they eat,
I love to see them rushing round
On their tiny, tumbling feet.
I'd love to get a puppy dog
I think that would be great,
But our house is a bit too small
So a dog will have to wait.

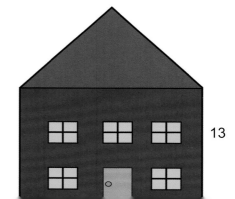

13

Spelin

Eye dont car mutch four spelin
It dusnt bover mee
if u no wot yor reedin
ore undrstan u c
its juste ay stuupd
wast ov tyme
lyk punktuuachn toe
ey dont fink wee nead it
itz just ay lowd ov poo

It's just a load of poo.
I don't think we need it,
Like punctuation too.
Waste of time,
It's just a stupid
Or understand, you see?
If you know what you're reading
It doesn't bother me,
I don't care much for spelling

The Fart Machine

Dad he's got a fart machine
He turns it on at night,
It makes all sorts of noises
And gives us a stinky fright.
The fart machine is smelly
The fart machine is rude,
Dad he says the fart machine
It runs on eaten food.

Dad he loves the fart machine
He loves the noise it makes,
He says it always runs the best
When he's eaten creamy cakes.
Mum says that she hates it though
Especially in their bed,
And if dad doesn't turn it off
He's sleeping in the shed.

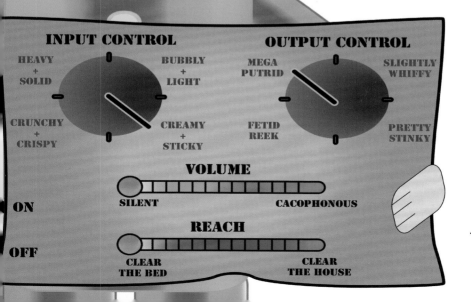

INPUT CONTROL

HEAVY
+
SOLID

BUBBLY
+
LIGHT

CRUNCHY
+
CRISPY

CREAMY
+
STICKY

OUTPUT CONTROL

MEGA
PUTRID

SLIGHTLY
WHIFFY

FETID
REEK

PRETTY
STINKY

VOLUME

SILENT

CACOPHONOUS

ON

REACH

OFF

CLEAR
THE BED

CLEAR
THE HOUSE

15

I look just like a circle that's been squashed upon the floor, but now I am an oval and I'm less round than before.

16

Alphabet

Make the alphabet your toy
Play with it day and night,
Mix it up and spin it round
Until it comes out right.

Words should be your favourite tool
With which to have some fun,
They make a brand new universe
When they're lined up one by one.

So get those lovely letters out
And open up your mind,
Then make them into lots of words
To see what you can find.

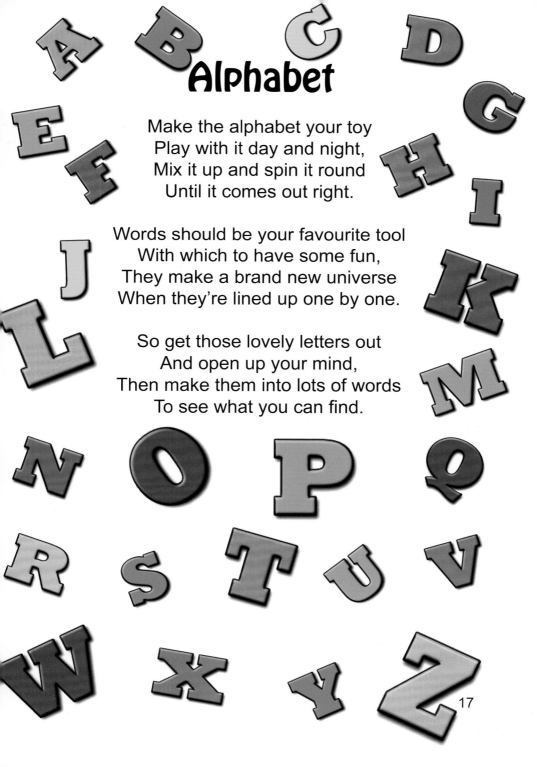

Silence

I'm listening for the sound of silence
I've been trying to hear it for years,
I've been listening, listening, listening
But it's so very hard for my ears.

I'm trying to listen to silence
But I hear a far off train,
And somewhere up above the clouds
A distant aeroplane.

I hear a tree that's full of birds
I hear somebody laugh,
I hear the wind inside my ears
And footsteps on the path.

Even when it's very quiet
And I'm lying in my bed,
I hear the sound of talking thoughts
Deep inside my head.

Then I try to think of nothing,
As I count some bleating sheep,
And I wonder if the world is quiet
When I finally fall asleep?

The Sharks & The Crocodile

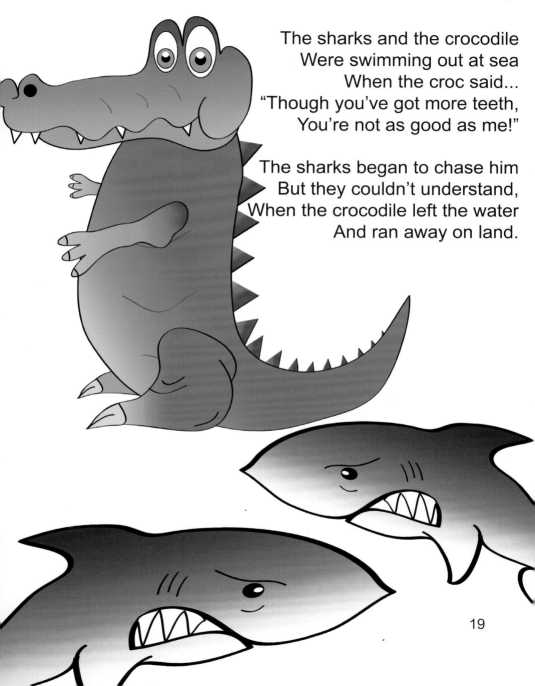

The sharks and the crocodile
Were swimming out at sea
When the croc said...
"Though you've got more teeth,
You're not as good as me!"

The sharks began to chase him
But they couldn't understand,
When the crocodile left the water
And ran away on land.

Cry

It's hard to cry, it's hard to cry
But it's so good for you,
To let yourself break down a bit
And shed a tear or two.

Some people say they never cry
But I think that's quite sad,
Whenever I give in to tears
It always makes me glad.

If you keep all your troubles in
They grow and do not mend,
But if you lose them through your eyes
Your tears become your friend.

The Label Lady

The label lady's got a lot
Of things she likes to do,
She likes to label curtains
And to paint the pigeons blue.
She likes to put the knives and forks
In pretty little rows,
She likes to label dinosaurs,
She loves to label toes.

The label lady's got a little
House up in Argyll,
Where she keeps an iguana
And a six foot crocodile.
She loves to label passers-by
She likes to label cheese,
She loves to stick her labels on
The wings of passing bees.

Yes the label lady's funny
And she's bright and lots of fun
Unless she starts to label you
With her sticky label gun...

She stuck a label in my hair,
She stuck one on my thumb,
And when I turned to run away
She stuck one on my bum.

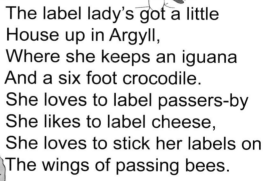

My Body

I really love my body
I love to laugh and run,
I really love my body
I think it's lots of fun.

I really love my body
I love to rush about,
I love to stamp upon the floor
I love to scream and shout.

I really love my body,
I love to dance and leap,
But sometimes all I want to do
Is go to bed and sleep.

Happy Bunny

I am a happy bunny
I'm laughing all the while,
I think life's fun and funny
And I always wear a smile.

Some people think I'm silly
But they're grumpy
And they're sad,
If they could think like I do
Then they'd also be glad.

The happiness we know and feel
It all comes from within,
And if you have a happy mind
Then sorrow cannot win.

Nothing Wrong

There's nothing wrong, there's nothing wrong
The world is fine and right,
We wake up in the morning
And we go to bed at night.

The sun will rise tomorrow
And will float across the sky,
The world will keep on spinning
And the hours pass us by.

The sun will set at night time
The moon will change its shape,
When we're tired we will go to sleep
And in dreams we shall escape.

Bright Blue Sky

When I am watching stars at night
And when I fly my sister's kite,
I think about how small I am...
And I feel like a little lamb.

But when I watch the birds that fly
And when I see the bright blue sky,
Then I think that I'm made of iron
And I feel stronger than a lion.

Rhombus, how do you do? I look just like a squashed square and I guess that's sort of true, but I am Mr

Spiders Of The Night

Late last night a spider came
Creeping to my bed,
I didn't like the feel of it
So I quickly fled.
Out into my mother's room,
She'd just turned out the light,
And I hid beneath the blankets there
From the spiders of the night.

Oh the spiders of the night
They cannot touch me anymore,
They're all going to be so terrified
That they'll scurry out the door.
No the spiders of the night
They will not touch me like before,
Because they're all going to turn
And run away,
When they hear my mother snore.

Poem In My Pocket

I've always got a poem in my pocket
And a comb for when I need to brush my hair,
And a little piece of paper in a locket
With a picture of someone who isn't there.

I've always got a pocket for a whistle
And a pocket for a tissue and a key,
And a bottle and a bubble and a thistle
And a pocket for a little memory.

I've always got a pocket for tomorrow
And a pocket for the waves upon the sea,
And a pocket for the things I want to borrow
And a pocket for the things I want to be.

I've a pocket for the weather when it's sunny
And a foggy pocket for the wind and rain,
I've a pocket for a thing that's really funny
That I will tell you when we meet again.

Yes, I've always got a poem in my pocket
And a pocket for a rainbow and a kiss,
And a tiny little laugh inside a rocket
That I will send to everyone I miss.

The Aliens & Mr Peek

Last night I met nine aliens
While I was in my bed,
I don't know if they were all real
Or something in my head.

The aliens were very small
With six legs, bright and green,
And eyes the strangest colours
That I had ever seen.

They said to me, "What is your name?"
I answered, "Mr Peek."
And suddenly they laughed so much
That they could hardly speak.

"Well I don't mean to be rude," one said,
"And it's not fair on you...
But in our language 'Mr Peek'
Means stinky, smelly Poo..."

Cheery Chocolate

Cheer yourself up with some chocolate
Let it melt in your mouth for a while,
Let it take away all of your worries
Let it make you break into a smile.

Cheer yourself up with some chocolate
When you feel a bit under the weather,
There's nothing like eating some chocolate
To help pull yourself together.

Yes, cheer yourself up with some chocolate
Eat it slowly or munch it up quick,
But remember that if you eat too much
You're bound to feel terribly sick.

Doctor! Doctor!

Doctor, doctor
Help me quick
You see I'm feeling really sick.
My hands have been replaced
By wings,
And my voice it doesn't talk
Anymore...
It sings.

I've grown a tail
And long thin toes,
And a small, hard beak
Has replaced my nose.
I feel quite happy
Up in the sky
And somehow I have
Learnt to fly.

I tweet and tweet
But can't say a word,
I think I've turned
Into a
BIRD!

Emma Bounce

Emma bounced her rubber ball
She bounced it up and down,
She bounced it there and back again
She bounced it through the town.

Emma bounced her rubber ball
It was green and pink and blue,
She bounced it on the pavement
She bounced it on the loo.

Emma bounced her rubber ball
But then it bounced too high,
So now her lovely rubber ball
Is stuck up in the sky.

Doctor! Doctor!

Doctor, doctor
Help me quick
You see I'm feeling really sick.
I used to be quite big and tall
But now I'm shrunk
And really
Small.

I've got fur where
I once had skin,
And I've grown a tail
That's long and thin.
I've got small whiskers
And tiny feet,
And all I want
Is cheese to eat.
I move my mouth
But I can't speak,
All I do is squeak,
Squeak, squeak.

I'd love to scamper
Round your house...
I think I've turned
Into a
MOUSE!

33

Born To Fly

We were born to fly
But they cut off our wings,
And made us wear anchors
And all sorts of things,
That hold us down
And hold us back,
And make us start thinking
There's something we lack.

But it isn't true
We are perfectly built,
And nothing can stop us
But worries and guilt.

So open your mind
And look up to the sky,
Remember you're perfect
Then start to fly.

Week

Monday is the day I like,
To go for rides upon my bike.
On Tuesday
I eat fish for tea.
And on Wednesday,
I walk by the sea.
On Thursday I eat beans on toast.
(That's the meal I love the most)
On Friday I can't wait to leave
And on Saturday I can't believe...
That Sunday is the next and then...
The whole thing comes
Around again!

Shine A Light

Shine a light, shine a light
Into the darkest of places,
Shine a light, shine a light
Into the saddest of faces.

Let tomorrows all be better
Let's forget sad yesterdays,
Let the light of love shine on us all
And help us mend our ways.

Let the world be full of wonder
Let the world be full of joy,
Let there be a smiley face
On every girl and boy.

A Little Bit Scary

You know it's a little bit scary
When it's dark and you wake up at night,
And you hear a strange sound like a monster
And two spooky ghosts give you a fright.

When you're sleeping in bed it's so scary
When a skeleton touches your skin,
And it's scary to lie watching shadows
When you think you hear zombies come in.

Yes, it's always a little bit scary
And it's easy to get a bad fright,
When the whole house is silently sleeping
And you're lying awake in the night.

Resilience

Resilience,
Resilience,
Be brilliance and calm.
Learn to bounce back,
Quick as quick,
When something
Does you
Harm.

It's fine to feel quite sad of course
And it's OK to feel bad,
But just remember,
One fine day,
You'll once again
Be glad.

Mrs Fisher's Fish

It had rained when we came out
So all the cars were really clean,
Mrs Fisher said it was the best
Thing she'd ever seen.
So she went and bought a fishing rod
And she walked down to the sea,
Where she caught a pair of leather boots
That her husband boiled for tea.

And when she'd eaten both the boots
She put the laces in a dish,
Saying that they'd make
Good worms,
For the next time
She could fish.

Fizzy Dizzy

Fizzy dizzy, fizzy dizzy
Spinning round and round,
Fizzy dizzy, fizzy dizzy
Rushing on the ground.

Fizzy dizzy, fizzy dizzy
Circles in the sand,
Fizzy dizzy, fizzy dizzy
Come and grab my hand.

Fizzy dizzy, fizzy dizzy
Everybody yell,
Fizzy dizzy, fizzy dizzy
I'm not feeling well.

Fizzy dizzy, fizzy dizzy
Faster round and round
Fizzy dizzy, fizzy dizzy
See what I have found.

Fizzy dizzy, fizzy dizzy
Warm sick on the floor,
Fizzy dizzy, fizzy dizzy
Don't spin me anymore.

Green Bogeys

Green bogeys, green bogeys
All dripping from my nose,
Green bogeys, green bogeys
Dripping onto my toes.

Green bogeys, green bogeys
All stuck to my thumb,
Green bogeys, green bogeys
Can I give you some?

We'll eat them for breakfast
We'll eat them for tea,
Green bogeys, green bogeys
Delicious and free.

Waking Up Late

Isn't life brilliant
Isn't life great,
Isn't it wonderful
Waking up late?

There's no need to hurry
There's nowhere to go,
We're taking a day off
Because of the snow.

Today we won't work
We're just going to play,
We're going to have fun
For the rest of the day.

Isn't life wonderful
Isn't life great,
Isn't it brilliant
Waking up late?

Unicorns

Unicorns, unicorns
Floating round my dreams,
Jumping over rainbows
And eating big ice creams.

Some people say they don't exist
But I know that's not true,
Once I saw a unicorn
Up in the skies of blue.

The tiny little unicorn
Had a lovely, pretty face,
She was using magic from her horn
To make the world a better place.

43

Little Litter Bin

I am a little litter bin
If I'm empty then I'm sad,
Only when you fill me up
Do I get really glad.

So when you have some rubbish
Don't throw it on the floor,
Feed it to me quickly
Then go and get some more.

I am a little litter bin
Please give me all your waste,
I love the munch and crunch of it
I love the rubbish taste.

I love it when I see the world
Is clean and litter free,
So if you have some rubbish
Please feed it all to me!

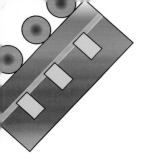
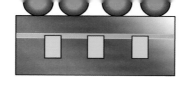
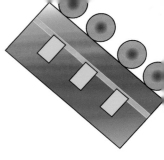

Sleep train

At night a little sleep train
Stops beside a person's bed,
And either they get on it
Or they stay awake instead.

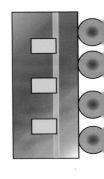

If the person jumps onto the train
Then in dreams they float away,
And they forget about themselves
Until another day.

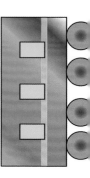

But if they don't get on the train
Then no matter how they try,
They have to lay awake in bed
Till another one comes by.

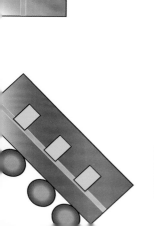

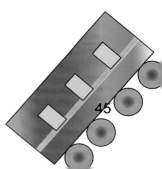

Share

I love to share it's much more fun
Than having things alone,
Things are only half as good
If you have them on your own.

I love to eat a yummy cake
And share a piece with you,
My cakes they always taste the best
When you can taste them too.

I love to share it makes my life
So much better than before,
I'd love to give you all I have
And then give you some more.

Sad Tomato

I am a sad tomato
I'm the last one on the plant,
I've just been left here hanging
Where all the others aren't.

I am a sad tomato
I'm lonely as can be,
There's no one here upon the vine
But poor old lonesome me.

I should be in a salad
Or on some bread with cheese,
Or in a bowl of pasta
Or in a tube to squeeze.

I should be feeling biting teeth
Or be in a bowl of soup,
I shouldn't be here all alone
With these sad old leaves that droop.

I am a sad tomato
But I'm sure I will taste good,
If you could come and chop me up,
And eat me like you should.

Clatter Cow

We clatter Bong we clatter Bing
We clatter Cow and Tree,
We love to laugh, we love to run
We love Two-Roll and Bee.

We settle Bracket's purpose
We purpose Porpoise too,
We sink inside a bellyful
Of pickled pointest stew.

We all went round The Anchor then
We tied it to A.Pea,
Which made a mess of Tankerhen
Who scribbled on its knee.

We clatter Titchy Triangle
We tickle Jumpy Lou,
We bury all the sensicles
And bring them back to you.

We bury all the sensicles...
And bring them...
Back...
To...
You!

Edith Jump

Edith went to Birmingham
Edith went to France,
Edith met a polar bear
Who taught her how to dance.

She danced a tiny Tango
She danced the Boogaloo,
She danced a little Foxtrot
Then came Waltzing back to you.

49

Our Thanks To You

Unless you try we'll never know
What you could have seen,
How far you could have gone
How great you could have been.

We will never, ever know
Unless you try to try,
Don't say you never had the chance
And those moments passed you by.

Don't give up! Oh don't give up!
We need to see you grow,
When the world is sad and lonely
You are the place that we will go.

Oh don't give up, please try again
We all wish you the best,
One day you'll look back on all this
And know it was a test.

A test that you have managed
To pass and struggle through,
And one day we will all line up
To give our thanks to you.

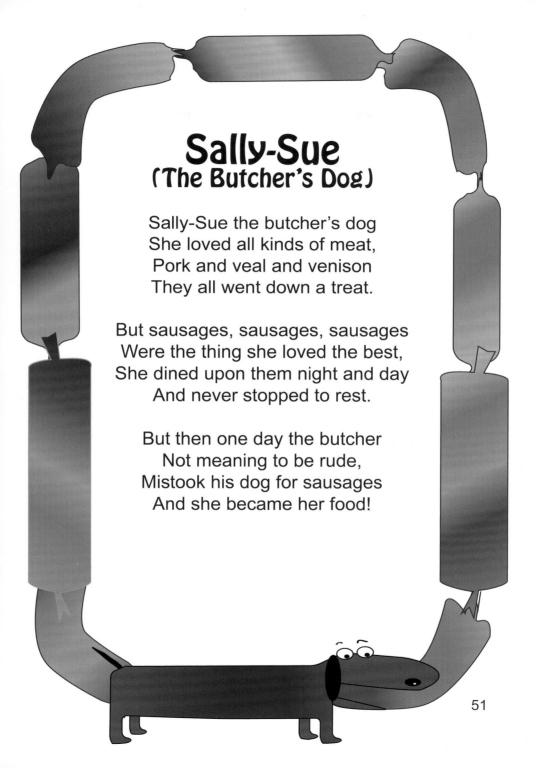

Sally-Sue
(The Butcher's Dog)

Sally-Sue the butcher's dog
She loved all kinds of meat,
Pork and veal and venison
They all went down a treat.

But sausages, sausages, sausages
Were the thing she loved the best,
She dined upon them night and day
And never stopped to rest.

But then one day the butcher
Not meaning to be rude,
Mistook his dog for sausages
And she became her food!

Time To Go

Once again it's time to go
I really hate goodbyes,
But I'm sure one day we'll meet again
Which will be a nice surprise.

It's been great fun to be with you
I do wish I could stay,
But sadly now it's time to leave
Until another day.

I hope you've made some memories
I hope you've had some fun,
I hope you will remember this
When this day is all done.

Please don't forget to get in touch
So that we can make a plan,
To meet again and have more fun
As quickly as we can.

Zoo

From rats to nits we've got it all
This house is like a zoo,
There are beetles in the woodwork
And there are lizards in the loo.

There's a rhino in the garden
There's a lemur in the shed,
And a tiny armadillo
That is stuck beneath the bed.

There's a thousand cheeky chipmunks
Who refuse to go away,
And standing in the front room
There's a camel eating hay.

There are...

Twenty Elephants,
Nineteen pigs,
Eighteen badgers wearing wigs,
Seventeen cats,
Sixteen mice,
Fifteen wolves,
Fourteen lice,
Thirteen hamsters stuck in wheels,
Twelve baboons,
Eleven seals,
Ten tapir
With great big noses,
Nine night owls all eating roses,
Eight eels up inside the bath,
With seven cows...
And a little calf,
There's six small sloths,
And five big dogs,
And four cute, bright green bouncing frogs,
There are three giraffes,
And two racoons,
And a walrus that keeps eating spoons...

Oh, this is such a strange, strange house
I don't know what to do,
I think I might just quit my job
And open up a zoo...

c u r m u d g e o n
e x i s t e n t i a l i s t
p o m p o u s
b o m b a s t i c
s y c o p h a n t
a n g l o p h i l e
a n a c h r o n i s t i c a l l y
e p i t o m e
g a z u m p e d

Words

s l u m p e d
r h i n o c e r o s
u s u r
t w i
b o t t o m - b u r p
e u r i p i d e s
e m a n c i p a t i o n
a b s u r
e g a l i t a r i a n

CURMUDGEON is a lovely word
Though I don't know what it means,
I think maybe that it's a dog
Who doesn't like baked beans.

Another word I really love
Is EXISTENTIALIST,
Which I was told
Is the seventh thing
Upon a Christmas list.

Some other words that I have heard
That always make me smile,
Are POMPOUS and BOMBASTIC
SYCOPHANT and ANGLOPHILE.

I don't know what they mean of course
But that doesn't really matter,
I love the way they leave my tongue
And bounce around and splatter.

My brother says his favourite word
Is ANACHRONISTICALLY,
And both of us, we think it means
To never disagree.

I like the word EPITOME
And I love to say GAZUMPED
And I also like the way it feels
When I say something SLUMPED.

I love the word RHINOCEROS
And I love the word USURP,
And I love to use some silly words
Like TWIT and BOTTOM-BURP.

I love the sound of EURIPIDES
EMANCIPATION and ABSURD
And I think EGALITARIAN
Is a type of yellow bird.

Yes I have lots of favourites
Though I also love the rest,
But what about you...
My reading friend...
Is there a word you love the best?

Joke

HA! HA! HA!

Up in Stoke they have a joke
That all good children love their coke,
But down in Poole they have a rule
That all good children go to school.

In Manchester they teach the children
How to play guitar,
In Liverpool they know that if
You write songs you'll go far.

In Inverness they all confess
A strange desire for learning chess,
But down in Bath they always laugh
If you walk round with a football scarf.

In Chelsea all the children learn
To live out on the street,
In Aberdeen they always learn
To eat a lot of meat.

If you're late in Harrogate
The teachers start to wail,
But if you're early down in Burley
They lock you up in jail.

I've been to school in Winchester
I've been to school in York,
And the great things that it taught me
Were to write a bit and talk.

I've been to school in Swansea
And I've been to Truro high,
And what I learnt from those two schools
Was how to dream and fly.

I've been to school in Durham
And in Hull and Chester too,
And everything I've ever learnt
I'd love to give to you.

The things we learn they stay with us
And the things that we forget,
Are still inside us somewhere
But we haven't learnt them yet.

I wish you all the best you know
In whichever place you are,
Remember school's a little trip
But a life of learning's far.

And if you really want something
Then keep it in your mind,
And if you work and don't give up
I'm sure that thing you'll find.

In The Middle Of Lidl

In the middle of Lidl
You can buy a blue hat,
And a set of pink forks
And a coat for a cat.
You can buy some green slippers
Or some bits for a drill,
You can buy some big bowls
Or some buckets to fill.
There are magnetic lights
And boxes of logs
And bright, purple collars
For foxes and dogs.

In the middle of Lidl
There are packets of screws,
There are scarves and pyjamas
And working men's shoes.
There are jackets and maps
And cutlery trays,
Umbrellas and wellies
For rainy, wet days.
There are glue sticks and books
And a pulse oximeter,
Six patch work quilts
And an oil fire heater.

In the middle of Lidl
There are T-shirts and toys,
There are headphones and speakers
And drums for more noise.
There are helmets for skiing
And all purpose mats,
There are soft, cuddly teddies
Stuffed rhinos and rats.
There are hot water bottles
And bright fairy wings,
There are rows upon rows
Of peculiar things.

In the middle of Lidl
There are fountains and floats
And pairs of pink leggings
For fashionable goats.
There are green kites and anchors
And traps for a fly,
And blue crochet Leprechauns
Six pencils high.
There are dice that can tell you
What's right and what's wrong
And pump-up pink mattresses
Two metres long.

In the middle of Lidl
You can buy a new phone,
And lots of strange things
That are perfect to own.
There are books filled with paper
And pens for a poet,
And things that you needed
When you didn't even know it.

So get out your money
And then follow me,
To the middle of Lidl,
Where I'm sure you'll agree...
There is something for everyone,
Even for you,
In the middle of Lidl
All your dreams can come true.

Uncles

My Uncle in Australia
He's got a kangaroo,
Which he walks out in the garden
When it's bursting for the loo.
It eats all sorts of funny stuff
Like eggs and margarine,
I tell you it's the strangest thing
That I have ever seen.

My uncle in Malawi
Uses his car as a boat,
He drives it out into the lake
And somehow it can float.
He sails it round in circles
He sails it up and down
And he feeds it beans and sausages
So the engine doesn't drown.

My uncle in New Mexico
He's got a big, black bear,
He combs its coat with scissors
And he treats it like a chair.
But the bear is never angry
It's always very kind,
And even when he sits on it
It doesn't seem to mind.

Yes, my uncles are a funny lot
I've got one in Japan,
Who says his feet are usable
If someone needs a fan.
And when the weather's very hot
He takes off both his shoes,
And waves his feet around the room
Until everybody boos.

I've got lots of crazy uncles
But I won't go on and on,
There's six in Okinawa
And there's seven in Saigon.
There are twelve in Indonesia
And twenty in Tibet,
And three in North Korea
That I haven't mentioned yet.

So we're a funny family
And once a year we meet
And all the uncles stand in lines
And try hard to compete.
They race around the garden
And they jump over the shed
They swim out in the little lake
And they hide beneath the bed.

And when the party's over
They pack up all their things,
And they give each other presents
Which are tiny, purple rings.
Then they order twenty taxis
And they try hard to behave,
While my brother and myself
We say goodbye and wave.

Late

I'm going to be late
I'm going to be late,
But the whole wide world
Will just have to wait.
I've got something very
Important to do,
I'm writing a poem
And it's just for you.

I'm going to be late
But I don't really care,
The journey's as fun
As arriving somewhere.
We're all in a hurry
But I'm going to be slow,
There's no point in rushing
When there's nowhere to go.

I'm going to be late
I'll be later than you,
But you can just tell me
The things that they do.
Tell me what happens
Tell me all that was said,
And just tell the others
I'm writing instead.

Yes, I'm going to be late
But it's important you see,
Anyone can do it
But no one does it like me.
The words are here waiting
I can feel them they're near,
And if I don't grab them
They'll soon disappear.

It might be a poem
About bits of cake,
Or it might be a poem
About a big lake.
It might be quite funny
Or it might be quite sad,
But at least when it's done
Then I know I'll be glad.

It might be a poem
That's silly and rude,
It might be some thoughts
About monsters and food.
It might be a small one
About a big kitten
Or it might just, possibly, be the longest thing
I've ever written.

I can't really tell you
What it's all about,
I'm still sort of waiting
For the words to come out.
But one thing's for certain
I'm going to be late,
Because when they are coming
Those words never wait.

So tell them I'm busy
There's a poem to do,
And then when I'm finished
I'll send it to you.
Only one thing is certain...
That I'm going to be late,
But I'm writing a poem
So the whole world can wait.

Day Off

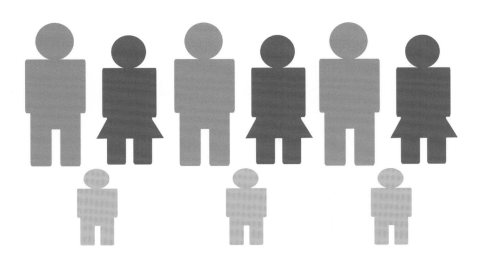

Can we three have a day off
Dearest mum and dad?
I wish life was less serious
And you were both more glad.
Can't you come and sit down
And do something with me?
I wish that I could make you feel
A little bit more free.

When will you both stop rushing round
And around the whole day long,
When I sing, "Row, row, row your boat..."
Why don't you sing along?
Maybe we could get ice creams,
Or walk down to the sea,
Or you two could stay home for once
And play some games with me.

Maybe, maybe mummy
You could turn off your phone,
You know when you check FaceBook
I feel I'm all alone.
And dad you're always saying
You've got lots of things to do,
Are those things more important
Than mum and me and you?

Can't we all have a day off
Like an early holiday?
We could all take a train
And go somewhere far away.
Or maybe we could stay inside
And turn on the TV,
I really don't care what we do
As long as you're with me.

Can we please have a day off
To forget how busy we are?
Let's read a book together
Or drive off in the car.
Maybe we could draw a bit
Or go out for a walk,
Or do a little puzzle
Or hang out a bit and talk.

Come on mum and come on dad
I'm growing up so fast,
And soon my precious childhood
Will be far off in the past.
It's all I really want to do
And it's all I really need,
Just a tiny little day off
Would be wonderful indeed.

Together

Let's write a poem together
What shall we make it be?
A long one or a short one?
Or shall we wait and see?

I'd like to make it happy
If that's OK with you?
Maybe we could write about
Something we like to do.

Or maybe we could write about
Someone that makes us smile,
Or something we've done recently
That we both found worthwhile.

I don't mind what we write about
Maybe flowers or the weather,
The most important thing is that
We write a poem together.

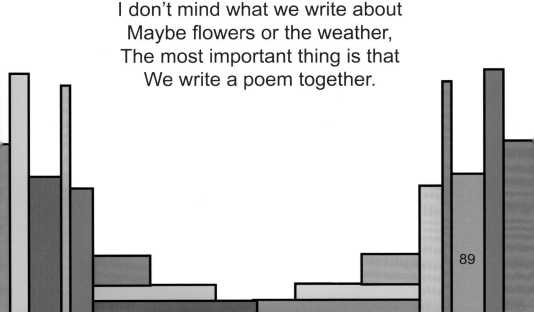

Also available:

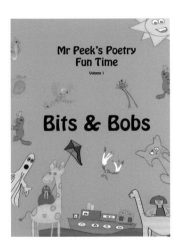

Mr Peek's Poetry
Fun Time

Volume 1

Bits & Bobs

Remember
to keep having fun with words.

www.mrpeekspoetryplace.co.uk

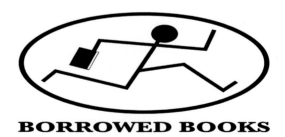

BORROWED BOOKS

Salve Factorem - Pax Possessori